INTRODUCTION

Rasboras are small fishes of the carp-minnow family (the huge family Cyprinidae) that abound in the fresh waters of India and Southeast Asia. The minnow family also includes such well-known aquarium fishes as the goldfish, the barbs, the danios, the so-called "flying barbs," and the labeos, as well as a host of others that have never been introduced to aquarists, or, having been introduced, never have achieved any degree of permanency in the hobby. Among the best, the rasboras are real gems. Some carps and minnows are great, hulking bottom feeders, or hungry predators on smaller fishes or, if of suitable size, are drab and colorless or pugnacious fin-nippers, but not so the rasboras. It is hard to imagine a more uniformly ideal group of aquarium fishes.

DISTRIBUTION OF THE GENUS *RASBORA*

The carp-minnow family has spread, since its probable origin over 80 million years ago in southeastern Asia or southern China, into temperate Asia, Europe, North America, and Africa, but, because of

A school of *Rasbora caudimaculata*. Fishes of the genus *Rasbora* are considered the ideal aquarium fishes because they are colorful, peaceful, easy to maintain on prepared foods, available from your local pet shop, and challenging to breed.

Photo by Aqua Press, MP&C Piednoir.

geographical barriers, has failed to reach South America and Australia. The genus *Rasbora* is one of the most successful and widely distributed, occurring in Pakistan, India, Sri Lanka (Ceylon), Bangladesh, Burma (Myanmar) , Thailand, Indo-China (Vietnam, Laos, Cambodia=Kampuchea), southern China (Kwangtung=Guangzhou, Yunnan, and Hainan I.), the Malay Peninsula, Borneo, Sumatra, Java, Bali, Lombok, Sumbawa, and southern

Mindanao and the Palawan chain in the Philippines.

Incidentally, a good modern large-scale map (of southern and southeastern Asia in this case) and a modern unabridged dictionary or encyclopedia, and, especially, a good fish encyclopedia, will be of real help to you in learning about fishes.

The *Pisces* volume of the serial *Zoological Record* (annual) is a huge, incredibly valuable resource. Later and current volumes are in CD-ROM. Ask your local librarian or, especially, the science librarian at your local university or natural history museum, for details.

HABITAT OF RASBORA

In their native range, rasboras are found in lowland and foothill streams, large rivers, ditches, rice paddies, ponds, lakes, and swamps, and are absent only from torrential mountain streams and oxygen-deficient waters. Like all cyprinids, they are strictly freshwater fishes. In most areas where they are found, organic matter washing into the streams keeps the water

Photo by Dr. Herbert R. Axelrod, circa 1960.

In this winding small stream in Malaysia, close to Singapore, both Chocolate Gouramis and *Rasbora heteromorpha* abound. These habitats on oil palm plantations no longer exist.

soft and acid. For example *R. heteromorpha* and *R. vaterifloris* generally are found in clear, acid, foothill streams, *R. gracilis* and *R. pauciperforata* in clear, brown-stained, very acid waters. But limestone areas with harder, more alkaline water may often have one or more species of *Rasbora*. Rasboras don't like brackish or polluted waters. The precise ecological requirements of most of the species of *Rasbora* are as yet unknown.

Photo by Dr. Herbert R. Axelrod, circa 1960.

Yeok Ong showing *Cryptocoryne* plants taken from the shallow stream in which *Rasbora heteromorpha* are to be found in Malaysia.

THE SPECIES OF *RASBORA*

As there are over 60 known species in the genus *Rasbora* Bleeker, 1859, it is obviously impossible to describe all of them here. Most of the species show the following color-pattern, or only a very slight modification of it: The back is darker (brownish or greenish) than the belly (usually silvery); there is a dark stripe (black, brown, or leaden-silvery) running from the snout, the eye, or the posterior edge of the gill cover, rearward along the middle of the side to the base of the caudal fin, and sometimes extending onto the central rays of the tail fin; this dark lateral stripe is bordered above by a narrower light metallic line (green-gold, gold, or coppery red); a dark line lies along the anal base, often extending as a thin streak along the lower edge of the caudal peduncle to the lower base of the tail fin; fins are typically clear, but in many cases there is a yellowish, orange, or reddish flush at the base of the dorsal, caudal, and anal fins. There are often dark margins to the tail and sometimes the dorsal and anal as well. The body shape is generally elongate, rather than deep. And remember, in the usual fish terminology, stripes run lengthwise, while bars or bands run vertically.

While many species of *Rasbora* have distinctive color-patterns (and some are distinctively shaped), a large number are so similar in size and coloration that identification is difficult without recourse to counting scales and fin rays and working out body-proportions. The taxonomy and classification of the rasboras and

Photo by Dr. Herbert R. Axelrod.

A well developed female *Rasbora heteromorpha*. This species is probably the most popular of all *Rasbora* species.

Rasbora espei is one of those species closely related to *Rasbora heteromorpha*.

Photo by Hans Joachim Richter.

rasbora-like fishes has yet to be worked out satisfactorily, most particularly for the complexes of larger species. Ichthyologists are laboring to untangle the problems, but collecting is expensive, time-consuming, and physically demanding under tropical conditions and countless streams have never had any collection made in them at all. Further, ichthyologists are dependent on the collections and publications of previous workers, and often influenced by the physical condition of early type material. A good example is the tangle involving the validity of *dusonensis, aurotaenia, tornieri, retrodorsalis,* and *myersi*. The type materials of the former two are in a poor state of preservation. The identity of *dusonensis* (described by the great Dutch ichthyologist Pieter Bleeker, a colonial army surgeon stationed in the Netherlands East Indies nearly 145 years ago, provides the key, in a situation where the "specimenus unici" (unique specimen=modern holotype) of Bleeker probably is, but may well not be, the actual holotype. There are morphological discrepancies between the "holotype" and other specimens collected for and identified by Bleeker, and between the specimens and the published descriptions (the original description and the latter expanded one in the *Atlas)* and the illustration in the *Atlas*.

The present work does not purport to be a generic revision, in whole or in part. I've tried to be "up to date", but new species are being described every year, and old ones renamed. The aquarist should not worry too much about all this! Just try to identify your rasboras as best you can! Enjoy them for their beauty and liveliness.

Species names are given below, with the author of the name (original describer) and the date of the original description. If the name of the describer is in parentheses, it indicates that the species has been placed in a genus other than the one in which it was originally described. The first rasboras were described in 1822 and placed in the genus *Cyprinus* Linnaeus, 1758 (the genus of the common carp!), and in the 1830's through the 1850's in *Leuciscus* Cuvier, 1816 (a genus of temperate zone minnows!) or in *Opsarius* McClelland, 1839 (an Indian-Indo-Malayan genus, a synonym of *Barilius* Hamilton, 1822; closer, but still not good enough!). Finally, in 1859, Bleeker created the genus *Rasbora*.

Most of the species of *Rasbora* are described below, with suggested English common names. Certain rare, isolated, or doubtful species are omitted. Abbreviations are as follows: **SL** — Sri Lanka, **Pa** — Pakistan, **I** — India, **Bang** — Bangladesh, **Bu** — Burma, **Th** — Thailand (Siam), **M** — Malaya Peninsula, **IC** — Indochina (**Vi**et **N**am, **L**aos, **K**ampuchea), **Su** — Sumatra, **Bo** — Borneo, **J** — Java, **Ba** — Bali, **Ban**—Banka=Bangka, **Bu**— Burma, **SC** — So. China, **P** — Philippines; **Cp** — circumpeduncular scale rows, **Pd** — predorsal scales, **Llp** — lateral line pores, **Lls** — lateral line scales, or scales counted along normal course of lateral line, **D** — dorsal fin, **A** — anal fin, **P** — pelvic fins (ventrals), **C** — caudal fin, **BP** — body proportions. Unless otherwise stated, the fins are essentially clear and colorless (though dorsal, anal, and caudal fins are often yellowish to reddish), the back is olive green to brownish, the belly silvery, a dark stripe runs from the opercle to the base of the tail fin, and the circumpeduncular scale rows are 12. Lengths given are for total length (i.e., including tail fin). The author's rating of the species as an aquarium fish is given as + (good), ++ (superior), +++ (extra special).

Rasboras agilis Ahl, 1937. Not a valid species. Described as a distinct species, it is now considered a synonym of *R. pauciperforata*. The species shown as *agilis* in Brittan (1971) has since been renamed *R. gracilis* by Kottelat (1987).

R. argyrotaenia (Bleeker, 1850). Silver-striped Rasbora. (A German name. Poor, as most rasboras have silvery-black

Photo by Dr. Herbert R. Axelrod.

Rasbora argyrotaenia has been in aquarists' tanks for more than 50 years as evidenced by this 1947 photograph.

Rasbora argyrotaenia.

Photo by Dr. Herbert R. Axelrod.

stripes.) **Th, M, IC, Su, Bo, J, Ph** (Palawan-Culion-Busuanga chain). To 7". Black metallic silvery stripe from eye or opercle. Light stripe metallic brassy gold. **D, A,** and **C** yellowish to orange, **C** with or without dark hind margin, which if present is not as pronounced as in *dusonensis, aurotaenia,* and *tornieri.* **Pd** 11-14, **Llp** and **Lls** 29-34, **Cp** 14. **BP** normal. Most widely distributed species of the Malayan subregion. Bleeker (1863) had many specimens from Java and from nowhere else, and some modern workers are coming to believe that the true *argyrotaenia* is found only there, and "argyrotaenia" from elsewhere are other, similar, species. Whether *argyrotaenia* is a single species with many races or a complex of several species remains to be determined. The Philippine Palawan chain race was originally described as *R. everetti* Boulenger, 1895.+

R. atridorsalis Kottelat & Chu, 1987. **SC** (Yunnan). 3". A straight dark brown to black band from top of opercle to caudal fin base, expanding slightly rearward, becoming nearly an oval blotch at its termination. A thick yellow stripe above it. **Pd** 13, **Llp** 31-32, **Lls** 31-32. Only *Rasbora* with five scale rows between mid-dorsal and lateral line scale rows. Markedly short-finned. +

R aurotaenia Tirant, 1885. Yellowtail or Gold-stripe Rasbora.**M, IC, Th, Su, Bo.** 4"-6". Weak dusky stripe from opercle to caudal base, broader and weaker than in *argyrotaenia*, bordered above by a thinner yellow to greenish stripe, which is still wider than the thin, intense longitudinal light metallic stripes of most other species. This is bordered above by a thin dark streak. Dark, thin axial streak along back half of body. **D. A,** and **C** yellowish, the latter often strongly so and with a black margin. **D** further back than in other species, originating 3 scales behind posterior base of pelvics, the dorsal-hypural base when carried forward falling behind eye. Two and one-half scale rows between lateral line row and mid-belly. Specimens from the turbid water of the Mekong in **Ka** and **Th**, and the Chao Phrya in **Th**, described by Smith (1945) as *retrodorsalis* are paler and deeper-bodied, and appear to be a race of *aurotaenia*, though they may represent a valid species. Rainboth (1996) considers *retrodorsalis* to be a valid species. **Pd** 14-15, **Lls** 33-35, **Llp** 33-35, **Cp** 14. ++

Drawn by John Quinn.

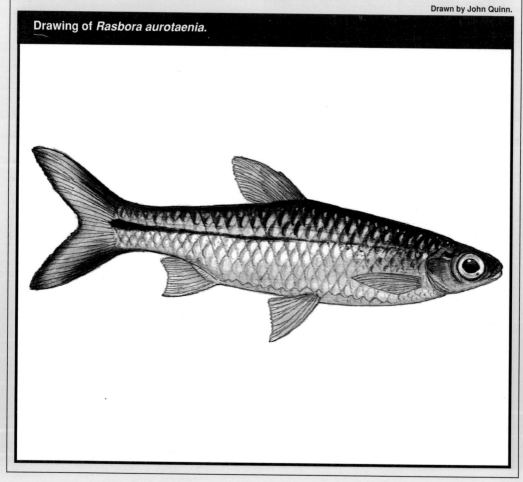

Drawing of *Rasbora aurotaenia*.

Rasbora axelrodi is a tiny, beautiful species. It is markedly dimorphic (females and males differ substantially). The males are more slender and shorter, but more intensely colored than the females.

Photo by Dr. Herbert R, Axelrod.

R. axelrodi Brittan, 1976. Neon Rasbora. **Su**(?), **Bo, Th** (s.), **IC** (Mekong Delta), **M**(?). 1" or less. A beautiful tiny fish, the "neon tetra" of cyprinids. Relatively blunt-headed and large-eyed. Moderately deep-bodied. Sexually dimorphic and dichromatic: males slenderer and much more brightly colored. An eye-width blue to emerald swath from eye to caudal base, lower flanks and belly copper red to carmine, anal fin membranes red, rays blackish brown (sexually mature males). Female colors much weaker. Males with large (really barely visible) tubercles on the head, cheeks, and shoulders, and a linear lateral "platform" along the lower jaw that bears larger multicuspid tubercles, similar to some small danios (brachydanios), such as *Brachydanio rerio*. Thus, this species may be a danioine rather than a *Rasbora* (Roberts, 1989). **Pd** 12, **Llp** 0, **Lls** 32. +++

Rasbora beauforti, the Stop-light Rasbora, is a doubtful species.

Rasbora axelrodi, the Neon Rasbora, is a lovely specimen that barely reaches a length of one inch.

R. baliensis Hubbs and Brittan, 1954. Lake Braten Rasbora. **Ba**—1-1 $^1/_2$". Large headed, skinny bodied, pale (the high volcanic lake, at 1,231 meters, not very productive?). Diffuse blackish streak from behind opercle to caudal base. Fins plain. **Pd** 11-12, **Lls** 28, **Llp** variously 16-26, **Cp** 12. +

Rasbora bankanensis, collected on Sarawak and photographed by Dr. Herbert R. Axelrod.

R. bankanensis (Bleeker, 1853). Banka=Bangka (Island) Rasbora. **M** (s. & e.), **Su?**, **Ban**. and adjacent islands off n.e. coast, **Bo** (s. w. and Sarawak). Blackish stripe from opercle, faint anteriorly, moderate posteriorly, broadly overlapping axial streak throughout. Anal fin usually with black subdistal oval bloch. Supra-anal/subpeduncular streak well-developed. Eye and head proportionally larger and preanal length shorter in total length (av. 65%) than in (paucisqulais). **Pd** 10-12, **Lls** 25-27, **Cp** 14. +

R. borapetensis. H.M. Smith, 1934. Thai Rasbora. **ThK.** 2". Black stripe from opercles, bordered above by a prominent gold streak. Caudal carmine basally. **Pd** 12, **Llp** 10-15, **Lls** 29-30, **Cp** 12. Probably the commonest Thai species. Found in ponds, lakes, rice-paddies, not in fast waters or big rivers. ++

R. borneensis Bleeker, 1860. Pale-straw Rasbora. S. **Bo**. slender, torpedo-shaped, pale straw-colored. Weak thin lateral streak on posterior half of body. Large punctate melanophores on

Drawing by John Quinn.

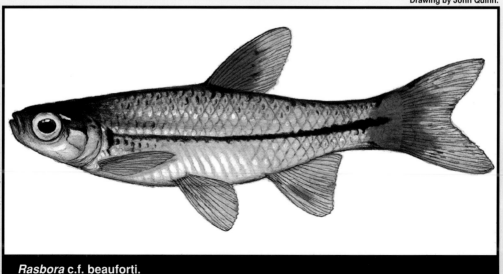

Rasbora c.f. beauforti.

R. beauforti Hardenberg, 1937. **Bo** (s.w.), **K**, **T** (Mekong Basin)? 2". black stripe fron snout to the tip of the central caudal rays, narrowest on the head and tail. It is difficult to identify this species from the original description and the types have been lost. Roberts (1989) regards this as a doubtful species. **Pd** 12, **Llp** 10, **Lls** 28-29, **Cp** 12. See *R.* sp. cf. *beauforti*, Stoplight Rasbora.

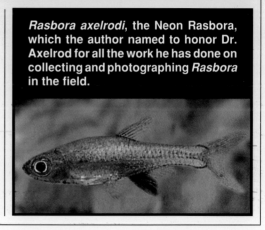

Rasbora axelrodi, the Neon Rasbora, which the author named to honor Dr. Axelrod for all the work he has done on collecting and photographing *Rasbora* in the field.

opercle and just behind it. Hind margin of caudal fin dusky, other fins plain. **Pd** 15-16, **Lls** 30-33, **Llp** 30-33 **Pd** 14. +

   R. brigittae Vogt, 1978. **Bo** (s.e.). Less than $^3/_4$". Body often somewhat reddish. A longitudinal black stripe from upper corner of operculum to a black spot at the mid-caudal base. Stripe broader anteriorly, with a yellow area bordering it above and below.

Rasbora borapetensis, a male, uppermost fish, with two females.

Photo by Burkhard Kahl.

Two views of *Rasbora brigittae*. This tiny fish is less than an inch in length. The fish on the left is a male; the fish on the right is a female.

Photos by Arend van den Nieuwenhuizen.

Outer margin of each caudal lobe fire red. Proportions and meristics much as in *urophthalmoides,* of which this is sometimes considered a race. ++

R. brittani Axelrod, 1976. Head-and-Tail Light Rasbora. **M, Bo.** 1 $^1/_2$"-2 $^1/_2$". Slender, much like *argyrotaenia*. Pointed snout. Silvery or brassy above, no lateral stripe, or only a faint one. A pupil-sized black spot at base of caudal fin, with a bright orange spot above it and another below. Iris orange or red around black pupil. **P, D,** and **A** colorless or slightly yellow. **Pd** 15, **Llp** 8-10, **Lls** 30-34. ++

Rasbora brittani, named to honor the author for his lifetime study of fishes in the genus *Rasbora.* *R. brittani* shows striking orange glints in the eye and caudal base, thus supporting the common name *Head-and tail Light Rasbora.*

Photo by Hans Joachim Richter.

***Rasbora caudimaculata*, the Greater Scissortail Rasbora, grows to 6 inches in length and makes a striking school fish in a large aquarium.**

Photo by Aqua Press, MP&C Piednoir.

R. caudimaculata Volz, 1903. Greater Scissortail. **M, Su, Bo.** 8". Broad, weak dark stripe. Tail yellowish, with subterminal cross stripe on each lobe, as in *trilineata*. Body darker, more greenish than *trilineata*, and body racier, less compressed on sides. Young with black tip to dorsal, black tips to caudal (*R. wijnbergi* Meinken, 1963, is based on juveniles of this species, as is *dorsimaculata* Herre, 1937). **Pd** 11-12, **Llp** 27-30, **Lls** 27-30, **Cp** 12. ++

R. caverii (Jerdon, 1849). 3"-4". **I** (Cauvery R. basin and adjacent southern India), **SL** (slow streams throughout, except in extreme north; absent in highlands above 600m.). Coloration paler and reticulate pattern indistinct, much less well developed than in *daniconius*. Narrow blackish stripe of moderate intensity from opercle to caudal base, thin goldish streak bordering above, a horizontal bar of dark pigment on opercle. Fins hyaline, caudal hind-margin unpigmented. dorsal fin set back than in *daniconius*, originating four scales behind th epelvic insertion. **Pd** 15-17, **Lls** 32-34, **Llp** 30-34, **Cp** 14. +

R. cephalotaenia (Bleeker, 1852). Porthole Rasbora. **M, Su, Bo.** 5". "Racy" body. Black stripe

Rasbora caverii, found in southern India and Sri Lanka, has a much more restricted range than *daniconius*. The dorsal fin originates well behind the level of the pelvics and is set back farther, so that the dorsal-hypural distance falls on the opercle, rather than on the eye as in *daniconius*.

Photo by Dr. R. Pethiyagoda.

A pair of *Rasbora cephalotaenia*, collected and photographed in Sumatra.

Photo by Dr. Herbert R. Axelrod.

Rasbora cephalotaenia. Frequently seen in aquaria, *R. cephalotaenia* is commonly known as the Porthole Rasbora. It has been found in Sumatra, Banka, Billiton, Malaysia and Borneo.

Photo by Edward Taylor.

from snout to posterior edge of opercle; in young continues to caudal base, in adults becomes a double row of parallel spots running in place of stripe. Secondary dark streak running on lower flank back from pectoral. Light stripe weak, gold. **C** central rays dark. **Pd** 13-14, **Llp** 32-34, **Lls** 32-34. ++

R. chrysotaenia Ahl, 1937. Gold-striped Rasbora. **Su** (?). 2". Black stripe from snout, light stripe greenish gold to reddish gold. Blue shoulder mark in some reflected light. Fins hyaline, posterior margin unpigmented. **BP** normal. **Pd** 12. **Llp** 5, **Lls** 26-27. **Cp** 12. ++

R. daniconius (Hamilton-Buchanan, 1822). Indian Rasbora. **I, Pa, SL** as for *caverii*, **Ban, Bu, Th**(?), **K**(?). 5". Black stripes from snout, continuing on opercle, and onto base of tail, then often onto medial tail rays, light stripe gold. **C** often faint yellow basally, faint dark margin. **Pd** 13-15, **Llp** 29-32, **Lls** 32-35, **Cp** 14. The most widespread Indian species, likely a complex of geographical races or closely related species. The Thai-Kampuchean form may be distinct. +

Rasbora chrysotaenia.

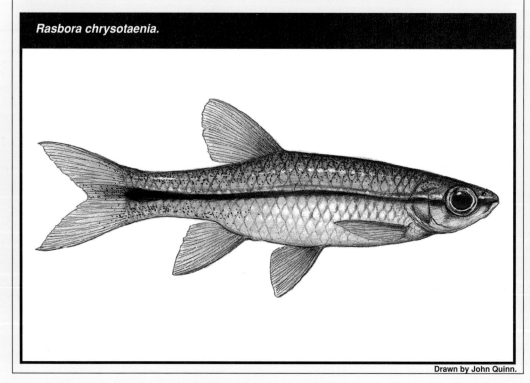

Drawn by John Quinn.

Above: Closeup of *Rasbora daniconius.* The black lateral stripe in this species may vary in intensity, but it is almost always deep black and always runs through the eye.

Bottom: Full view of *Rasbora daniconius*, which is widely distributed in the Indian subcontinent. Notice that in this individual the golden stripe above the black stripe is more pronounced than in the individual shown above; the golden stripe tends to be more variable than the black stripe.

R. dorsinotata Kottelat, 1982. **Th** (Chieng Rai Province). 1¹/₂"-2". A black stripe from just behind opercle to caudal base, expanding posteriorly to end in an oval. Faint streak along anal base. Black tip to dorsal. Caudal reddish with black posterior margin. **Pd** 12, **Llp** 27-28, **Lls** 27-28, **Cp** 12 . +

pale yellowish to bright rosy red, with a narrow blackish margin. Dorsal-hypural distance, when carried forward, falling on eye; 2 ¹/₂ scales from lateral line scale rows from lateral line row to midbelly. **Pd** 12-14, **Llp** 29-31, **Lls** 29-31, **Cp** 14. See *aurotaenia, myersi,* and *tornieri.* ++

Rasbora dorsiocellata, the Black Flag Rasbora, is, perhaps, the most easily identified of all **Rasbora** species. When in good health and under proper lighting, **R. dorsiocellata** shows a metallic green tinge.

Photo by Klaus Paysan.

R. dorsiocellata Duncker, 1904. Emerald-eye Rasbora, High-Spot Rasbora, Pirate-flag Rasbora. 1-1 ¹/₂" **M, Su, Bo.** 2 ¹/₂". Body greenish, sometimes pale olive or brownish, no stripe. Eye bright emerald green. **D** with large round intense black spot. **Pd** 10-12, **Llp** 6-27, **Lls** 28-29. **BP** normal. +++

R. dusonensis (Bleeker, 1851). Rosefin Rasbora, **Th, M, Su, Bo, IC.** 6". Weak dusky stripe from opercle, broader and more diffuse than in *argyrotaenia*, bordered above by a weak yellowish-gold streak. **D** well behind ventrals. **C**

R. einthovenii (Bleeker, 1861). Pearl Rasbora. **M, Su, Bo.** 4". Beautiful pearly mauve flush over brownish body. Black stripe from snout, ragged along lower edge, but below central axis of body. Light stripe very faint, goldish. **C** central rays blackish. Fins rather rounded. **BP** normal, but peduncle thickish. **Pd** 12-14, **Llp** 23-31, **Lls** 29-32, **Cp** 12. *R. labuana* Whitley, 1957, from Labuan I., Borneo, and *R. vegae* Rendahl, 1926, from Labuan I. and Sabah, Borneo, are synonyms of this species. ++

Rasbora dusonensis.

Drawing by John Quinn.

Rasbora dusonensis is a racy Rosefin Rasbora which reaches 6 inches in length thus making it suitable only for large aquaria.

Photo by Edward Taylor.

Rasbora einthovenii, the Pearl Rasbora, features a slightly downward-bowed dark lateral stripe which makes this an easy *Rasbora* to identify.

Photo by Dr. Herbert R. Axelrod.

Rasbora einthovenii.

Photo by Edward Taylor.

R. elegans Volz, 1903. Two-spot Rasbora or Elegant Rasbora. **M, Su, Bo.** 6". Body often suffused with yellowish or warm reddish brown. A rectangular spot in mid-side below dorsal, a round spot at base of tail fin; these sometimes connected by dark line (*R. aprotaenia* (Java), *R. e. bunguranensis* (Bunguran I), *R. e.*

R. espei Meinken, 1967. "T-bone" or "Lamb-chop" Rasbora. **Th** (s. and peninsula/s. Mekong basin). 1 $^1/_2$". Coloration and patterns similar to *heteromorpha*, but black side-marking cleaver-shaped instead of hourglass-shaped. Body less deep than in *heteromorpha* of which it may be a subspecies. **Cp** 11, **Ll** 23-25, **Llp**

Rasbora elegans differs from *R. kottelati* by its background color and the position of the lateral blotches.

Photo by Edward Taylor.

spilotaenia (Sumatra), *etc.;* are these specimens a form of *elegans* or hybrids of *elegans* and *sumatrana?*). Kottelat and Whitten (1993) consider all three distinct species **D, C,** and **A** often yellowish, **C** sometimes with blackish tips. **Pd** 11-13, **Llp** 26-29, **Lls** 26-29, **Cp** 12. ++

R. ennealepis Roberts, 1989. Found in s. **B.** (Kapuas R. Basin) Resembles *R. bankanensis* in basic form and scale counts. Heavy, pronounced reticulate pattern, denser broader black swath, especially posteriorly **Pd** 9, **Lls** 24, **Llp** 24-25, **Cp** 12 +

Rasbora elegans, the Two-spot or Elegant Rasbora.

Photo by Dr. Karl Knaack.

Rasbora gracilis.

Photo by Klaus Paysan.

Rasbora hengeli closely resembles *Rasbora heteromorpha* and may only be a race of this species.

Photo by Edward Taylor.

A school of *Rasbora hengeli* makes an attractive presentation.

Photo by Hans Joachim Richter.

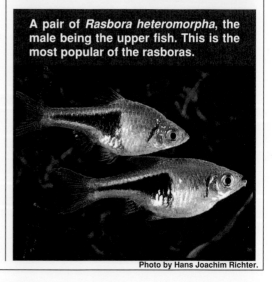

A pair of *Rasbora heteromorpha*, the male being the upper fish. This is the most popular of the rasboras.

Photo by Hans Joachim Richter.

R. hengeli Meinken, 1956. "T-bone" Rasbora. **Su.** 1 $^1/_2$". Resembles a less deep-bodied version of *heteromorpha*, and has a much narrower cleaver-shaped black area which occupies, however, the same position. It has been reported that it has been crossed with *heteromorpha*, so it may well be only a subspecies of the latter. **L.l.s** 22-24, **L.l.p.** 5-6, **Cp** 10. +++

R. heteromorpha Duncker, 1904. Harlequin Rasbora. **M, Su, Bo, Th.** 2". Body deep, sides compressed. Basic color coppery red. A striking broad black wedge on posterior half of body, its apex directed backward, and bordered above by a faint coppery gold line. A black streak along base of anal, continuing along lower edge of caudal peduncle. Fins reddish, often with dusky rays. **Pd** 10-11, **Llp** 6-9, **Lls** 26-27, **Cp** 10. Once called "*The* Rasbora." +++

Rasbora hobelmani.

Drawn by John Quinn.

R. hobelmani Kottelat, 1984. **Th, K** (middle Mekong basin); also Chao Phrya basin in **Th**. 1". Hobelman's Rasbora. Moderately deep, short body, thickish caudal peduncle. Short headed, round snout. Diffuse lateral stripe from opercle to caudal base, widest in front of caudal fin, thin on the afterbody, and ending in a small precaudal spot. Well-developed reticulate pattern. Black supra-anal streak running back along bottom of caudal peduncle. Fins slightly dusky, but caudal margin not blackish. **Pd** 11-12, **Lls** 25-28, **Llp** 25-28, **Cp** 12. +

R. hubbsi Brittan, 1954. Hubbs' Rasbora. North **Bo**. 1 1/2". Size, counts, and coloration as in *meinkeni* and *trifasciata*, but **Cp** 14. **Pd** 10-11, **Llp** 25-29, **Lls** 26-28. +

R. jacobsoni Weber & de Beaufort, 1916. Jacobson's Rasbora. **Su.** 2 1/2". General color brownish. A black or deep-brown stripe from snout, broadest below dorsal, a gold stripe above it, a secondary dark streak on flank. **D** and **A** washed with brown; **C** yellowish basally, then dusky, then tips colorless. **BP** normal, caudal peduncle thickish, fins rounded. **Pd** 12, **Llp** 24-27, **Lls** 26-28. ++

R. johannae. Siebert and Guiry 1997. Joan's Rasbora. **Bo** (s.e.). 1 1/2 ^{n}. Moderately deep-bodied anteriorly. Dark lateral stripeweak and diffuse anteriorly, becoming stronger posteriorly, ending in a black blotch on caudal base. Well-developed supra anal streak. Reticulate pattern weak, strongest on midbody. Fins plain. **Pd** 12, **Lls** 25, **Llp** 20, **Cp** 12. +

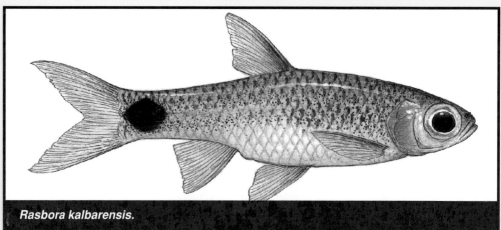

Rasbora kalbarensis.

Drawn by John Quinn.

R. kalbarensis Kottelat, 1991. One-spot Rasbora. **B.** 1". No lateral stripes, sides plain. A fairly well-developed reticulate pattern on anterior two-thirds of body. A round black blotch the size of the eye at the end of the caudal peduncle. Anterior caudal rays dusky at their bases. **Pd** 14, **Llp** 0, **Lls** 27-28, **Cp** 12. +

R. kalochroma (Bleeker, 1850). Red-ember Rasbora. **M, Su, Bo.** 2-3", occasionally 4". Body and **C** bright brick to cherry red, **D** and **A** same, but paler. Two large black blotches on mid-side, one behind gill cover, one above anal. **BP** normal, but thickish caudal peduncle lacks the pre-caudal spot. **Pd** 11-12, **Llp** 29-32, **Lls** 28-31, **Cp** 12. +++

R. kottelati Lim, 1995. **Bo,** n.w. (Sarawak). 3 $^{1}/_{2}$". Closely resembles *R. kalochroma*, but has a prominent vertically oval precaudal spot (absent in the latter), and lacks the prominent blackish mid-caudal rays. From

Rasbora kalochroma showing the distinct reddish-orange flush to the fins.

Photo by Dr. Herbert R. Axelrod.

Rasbora kalochroma in a perfect setting.

Photo by Aqua Press, MP&C Piednoir.

the photograph in Lim (1995), the present fish may be somewhat slenderer and less intensely red, but this is an extremely attractive species. **Pd** 12-13, **Lls** 30, **Lls** 28, **Cp** 12. Apparently separated from the widely-ranging *kalochroma* by the seaward end of the Kapuas Hulu range of extreme southern Sarawak, which species occurs just to the north.

R. lateristriata (Bleeker, 1823.) Java Rasbora. **J, Ba**(?). 4". Black stripe from opercle. Light stripe gold. **C** and **D** pale yellowish or reddish basally. **Pd** 12-14, **Llp** 29-33, **Lls** 29-33, **Cp** 12. The true *lateristriata* apparently is not found outside Java, unless *trifasciata* and *meinkeni* prove to be subspecies of it. +

R. laticlavia Siebert and Richardson 1997. **Bo.** Large specimens may reach 6". This species has basically the same coloration as *R. argyrotaenia*,

Rasbora kottelati closely resembles *Rasbora kalochroma*. *R. kottelati*, though, has a prominent precaudal spot lacking in *kalochroma*.

Photo by Tan Heok-Hui.

usually being placed in the synonymy of that species. However, there are subtle differences: while both have 14 circumpeduncular scales, in *laticlavia* the black lateral streak extends forward to about the level of the pelvic fins and fades out; there is a prominent sprinkling of black dots on the operculum and the anterior flanks (somewhat wider than the orbit), lying below the black streak; the lateral line pores run diagonally downward *straight* to the origin of the pelvic fins. In *argyrotaenia*, the dark streak extends all the way up to the opercle; the sprinkling of black dots is only as wide as the pupil and runs only as far back as the level of the pelvics; and the lateral line passes backward and downward in a shallow *bow* to above the level of

Rasbora laticlavia.

Drawn by John Quinn.

the pelvic origin. **Ll** 27-30, **Ll** 27-30, **Pd** 12, **Cp** 14. This species occurs together with (i.e., sympatrically) *argyrotaenia* in some Bornean Rivers. +.

R. leptosoma (Bleeker, 1855). Slender Rasbora. **Su.** 4". A broad blackish-silvery swath from opercle to caudal base. Fins hyaline-yellowish. Dorsal originating over rear of caudal base. **Pd** 12-13, **Lls** 31-32, **Llp** 31-32, **Cp** 12. It is currently impossible to tell if this is a valid species. Most aquarium records are really for *pauciperforata*.

R. maculata Duncker, 1904. Spotted Rasbora. Also variously called Pygmy Rasbora, Dwarf Rasbora, or Red Rasbora, or combinations thereof. **M, Su.** 1". Brownish-red, but bright orange red in breeding color. Two black spots, one in mid-side above pelvics and at anal base, and often another black spot on mid-side above anal base (the two latter spots often connected into a single dumbbell-shaped blotch). **C** reddish; **D** and **A** reddish with black triangles at anterior bases, and blackish tips. **BP** normal. **Pd** 11-13, **Llp** 0, **Lls** 26-30, **Cp** 10-12. +++

R. meinkeni de Beaufort, 1931. Meinken's Rasbora. **Su, M**(?), **Bo**(?). 3 $^1/_2$". Often a yellowish caste. Black stripe from opercle, gold stripe above it. **D** and **C** yellowish basally. **BP** normal. **Pd** 12-13, **Llp** 28-29, **Lls** 26-28. This may be the Malayan-Sumatran representative of *trifasciata* Popta, 1903, originally described from Borneo. *R. tobana* Ahl, 1937, supposedly from volcanic Lake Toba in Sumatra, is apparently a synonym of *meinkeni*. ++

Rasbora maculata, the tiny 'class' of the aquarium trade since the turn of the century (1900). It is also one of the smallest of freshwater fishes.

Photo by Aqua Press MP&C Piednoir.

THE SPECIES OF RASBORA

Rasbora meinkeni might possibly be *R. trifasciata*. The female is the lower fish.

Photo by Dr. Herbert R. Axelrod.

R. merah Kottelat, 1991. **Bo** (s.). ³/₄". Bears a superficial resemblance to *R. maculata*. Background reddish. An elongated oval black blotch in middle of anterior side. A smaller blotch at base of anal fin, a still smaller blotch at midpoint of caudal base. A ragged thin black line down mid-body from level of anal blotch to an eye-width of

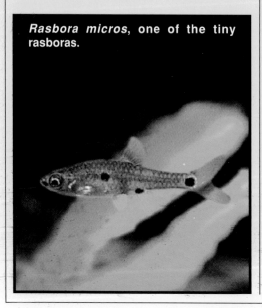

Rasbora micros, one of the tiny rasboras.

caudal-base blotch. Black streaks along anterior dorsal and anal rays. **Pd** usually 12, **Llp** 0, **Lls** usually 27, **Cp** 12. ++

R. micros Kottelat & Vidthayanon, 1993. **Th** (n. central). ¹/₂". Body light brown to reddish brown. Three black spots the size of the pupil, one a little above mid-side an eye diameter in front of dorsal origin, the second above rear half of anal base, the third just in front of caudal origin (mid-precaudal spot). **Pd** 10-12, **Llp** 0, **Lls** 21-23, **Cp** 12 (rarely 14). Found only in two widely

Rasbora merah, one of the diminutive species.

separated marsh pools in northern Thailand. Possibly a rare isolated relict of an ancestral *maculata*-type rasbora. Kottelat (1993) has set up the genus *Bororas* (an anagram of *Rasbora*) to include *brigittae, maculata, merah, micros,* and *urophthalmoides*. Until a thorough revision, I prefer to leave these species in *Rasbora*. +

R. myersi Brittan, 1954. Myers' Rasbora, Silver Rasbora. **M, Su,**

Rasbora micros.

Rasbora myersi is a large silvery rasbora without well-defined color markings.

Photo by Edward Taylor.

Rasbora myersi.

Photo by Dr. Herbert R. Axelrod.

Bo, IC, Th. 6". Weak to moderately strong, broad leaden stripe from opercle to caudal base, weak gold stripe above it. **C** grayish to slightly yellowish, with a narrow dark margin. Three and one-half scales between lateral line row to midbelly. Dorsal fin originating over posterior base of pelvic fins. Dorsal-hypural distance, when carried forward, falling on front to middle of eye. **Pd** 12-14, **Llp** 29-31, **Lls** 29-31, **Cp** 14. +

    R. nigromarginata Meinken, 1957. Fire Rasbora. **SL.** 2". Body and lower caudal lobe purplish-red, upper part of peduncle and caudal lobe blue-green. **D** and **A** with first rays black, remainder of fins bluish; **D** and **A** high, extremely so in male. Body deep, sides compressed. **Pd** 13-14, **Llp** 1-5 (usually 1), **Lls** 27-29. This species has been considered by recent workers to be a color morph of *R. vaterifloris.* +++

    R. pauciperforata Weber & de Beaufort, 1916. Red-line Rasbora. **M, Su, Bo.** 2 $^1/_2$". Brownish, with weak chocolate stripe from opercle, bordered above by bright neon-red stripe from snout. **Pd** 13-14, **Llp** 5-10, **Lls** 30–34. **BP** normal, fins high and pointed but not nearly as much as in *gracilis.* +++

Rasbora pauciperforata, the Red-line Rasbora, is medium small, beautifully colored with a copper-red lateral streak. This is a peaceful, lovely species and highly recommended for the home aquarium.

Photo by MP&C Piednoir Aqua Press.

Artist's rendition of a *Rasbora* tentatively identified as *R. paucisqualis* on the basis of its low scale count, but probably an undescribed species from the Mekong.

Drawn by John Qinn.

R. paucisqualis Ahl, 1935. Big Scaled Rasbora. **M** (s.), Singapore, T?, **K**? 2 $^1/_2$". Dark stripe on posterior half of body, fading out anteriorly, gold stripe above it. Dark stripe slightly overlaps axial streak; anteriorly it diverges to well below the axial streak. Supra-anal/subpeduncular streak well developed. Usually a dark streak on the outer third or half of the longest (third) unbranched anal ray. Preanal distance longer in total length (av. 70%) than in *bankanesis*, and head and eye proportionately smaller. Body a bit deep. **Ps** 10, **Lls** 24-28 (av. 26), **Llp** 22-27 (av. 25), **Cp** 12.

R. pavei Tirant, 1885. Cottonswab Rasbora (from the shape of the black stripe). **Th, IC.** "5". Body shape and scale counts essentially as in *sumatrana*, of which this has usually been considered a subspecies or race. It may be a valid species. *Rasbora cheroni* Fowler (1937) is

apparently the same species. Strong narrow black streak from opercle at level of top of the pupil to center of caudal base, where it widens to a prominent triangular blotch. Prominent reticulate pattern. Elongate supra-anal blotch. Blackish tips on caudal fin may or may not be present.

R. philippina Günther, 1880. Philippine Rasbora. **Ph** (Mindanao). 3 $^1/_2$". Dark stripe from opercle, a gold stripe above, former weaker than in *argyrotaenia*. **C** yellowish basally. **BP** normal, but a trifle deep. **Pd** 11-13, **Llp** 29-32, **Lls** 29-32, **Cp** 14. +

R. rasbora (Hamilton-Buchanan, 1822). Bengal Rasbora. **I, Bu, Th** (rare). 3 $^1/_2$"-4". The type-species of the genus. Black stripe from opercle to caudal base, gold stripe above. **C** yellowish with blackish posterior margin. **Pd** 12, **Llp** 29-31, **Lls** 27-31. **Bp** normal. Sometimes mistaken for *argyrotaenia*, sometimes for *sumatrana*. Its range centers in the lower Ganges and adjacent India, and extends to eastern Burma. +

R. reticulata Weber & de Beaufort, 1915. Chain Rasbora. **Su,** Nias I. 3". Extremely heavy chain-mail pattern on sides. No stripes. Body heavy. **Pd** 12-13, **Llp** 8-18, **Lls** 27-28. +

R. rutteni Weber & de Beaufort, 1916. Big-Scaled Rasbora or Rutten's Rasbora. **Bo, M**(?), **S**(?). 3". Black stripe on posterior half of body, fading anteriorly, **D** and **C** rosy. Body a bit deep. **Pd** 10, **Llp** 24-26, **Lls** 26-29. *R. paucisqualis* is possibly of this species. (*R. sarawakensis* Brittan, 1951, is closely related and physically similar.) +

R. sarawakensis Brittan, 1951. Sarawak Rasbora. **Bo** (Sarawak). 2". Body and caudal

peduncle relatively short and deep. Head broadly conical in side view, snout pointed, upper lip slightly overhanging. Eye large. Head and eye relatively larger than in *trifasciata, meinkeni,* and *bankanensis*. Black lateral stripe fom opercle to caudal base, slightly bowed upward. Dark blotch on opercle. Thin, but definite, dark supra-anal streak. **Pd** 11, **Lls** 26-27, **Llp** 25-26, **Cp** 12. +

R. semilineata Weber & de Beaufort, 1916. Weak-Striped Rasbora. **Bo, Ph**(Palawan I.). 2". Body brownish-yellow. Weak, diffuse dark stripe on side, spot at base of tail. Fins yellowish. **Pd** 11-13, **Llp** 5-15, **Lls** 27-31, **Cp** 10-12. *R. taytayensis* Herre, 1924, is a synonym. +

R. somphongsi Meinken, 1958. Dwarf Siamese Rasbora. **Th.** $1^1/4$".

Rasbora somphongsi is the smallest rasbora in continuous trade among hobbyists. It was named for the late Somphongs Lekaree who was with Dr. Axelrod when he collected and photographed this species. The female is the lower fish.

Photo by Dr. Herbert R. Axelrod.

A squared-off black stripe begins below front of dorsal; black streak along anal base, with a "jog" upward anteriorly; small black triangular patch of pigment at upper and lower base of caudal fin. A golden line above dark lateral stripe, beginning at opercle, another weaker one below it outlining upper margin of body cavity. Fins yellowish. **Pd** 10 or 11, **Llp** 0, **Lls** 23-24, **Cp** 10. **BP** normal. +++

R. spilocerca Rainboth & Kottelat, 1987. Yellow Scissortail, Dwarf Scissortail. **Th, VN, K.** 1", usually less. Body with a strong yellowish caste, a prominent

anterior subdistal black blotch, a similar one often present in **A. C** yellowish, with a diagonal black subterminal bar on each lobe, not outlined in white as in *trilineata*. **Pd** 12, **Llp** 4-8, **Lls** 27-30, **Cp** 10. ++

R. steineri Nichols & Pope, 1927. Chinese Rasbora. 3". **SC**(southeast, and Hainan I.), n. **IC**(?). Black stripe from opercle, bordered above by gold stripe. Base of **D** and **C** yellowish to rosy, sometimes a deep carmine, which may spread forward on the lower caudal peduncle. **BP** normal, a bit thick peduncled. **Pd** 12-13, **Llp** 28-32, **Lls** 28-32. ++

Rasbora spilocera, the Dwarf Scissortail Rasbora, is a tiny pale-yellow species. Its lack of color has not made it an aquarium favorite.

Drawn by John Quinn.

black narrow mid-lateral stripe. A large black spot covering bases of most caudal rays and extending over about two-thirds of the middle rays. A clear gap about one scale-width between end of stripe and caudal spot. Reticulate pattern well developed only above lateral line. Heavy dark streak along anal base and backward to lower caudal fin origin. **D** with

R. subtilis Roberts, 1989. Skinny Scissortail. **Bo** (Kapuas R. system). 1 $^3/_4$". Body bluish-green, caudal fin lobes yellow with diagonal black subterminal bars. A thin blackish mid-lateral streak on rear half of body, ending in a median black spot at caudal base (sometimes absent). Eye large. **Pd** 14-17, **Llp** 8-10, **Lls** 34-36, **Cp** 14-16. Much more slender-bodied and torpedo shaped than other "scissortails," such as *trilineata*, *spilocerca*, and *caudimaculata*. ++

R. taeniata Ahl, 1922. This is not a valid species. The holotype, in dried-out condition, is not a

Rasbora steineri is from southeastern China and the island of Hainan. It appears frequently in the aquarium trade.

Photo by G.J.M.Timmerman.

R. sumatrana (Bleeker, 1852). **Th, M, Su Bo, IC.** 6". Highly variable in color pattern. May have a dark stripe, a stripe posteriorly only, or none at all; if present, stripe may or may not end in a spot at base of tail; spot may be present without stripe. Streak above anal may be variable in shape, and is often absent. Tail may or may not have dark margin or dark tip to lobes. Bleeker's (1863) specimens were from *sumatra*, and it is likely that many of the variable populations from other localities are other species (see *R. pavei*). **Pd** 12-13, **Llp** 27-32, **Lls** 27-32. +

Rasbora but probably a cyprinodontoid (killifish), according to Kottelat (1991). Brittan (1954), having not seen the type but trying to match Ahl's description to a living fish species, considered *taeniata* to be valid and included Ahl's *agilis* as a synonym. Later (1971), he considered *taeniata* to be unrecognizable, but recognized *agilis* as valid and as being the species most aquarists were calling "*taeniata*." *R. agilis* is now recognized as a synonym of *pauciperforata*, and the fish called *agilis* in Brittan (1971) is now called *gracilis*.

Rasbora sumatrana is a widespread species which shows considerable variation in the length and intensity of the dark lateral stripe.. This stripe may even be missing!

Photo by Dr. Karl Knaack.

Rasbora tornieri is a distinctively colored fish which is often confused with several others rasboras including, but not limited to *R. taeniata, R. agyrotaenia* and *R. dusoniensis.*

Photo by G.J.M.Timmerman.

R. tawarensis Weber and DeBeaufort, 1916. **S**, only Lake Tawar. 4-6". Slender and somewhat large-headed. Jaws slightly hooked. Dark axial streak posteriorly. Weak spot on caudal base. Diffuse dusky band from opercle to caudal base. **Pd** 11-12, **Lls** 30-32, **Llp** 30-32, **Cp** 12. +

R. tornieri Ahl, 1922. **B, M, IC, S**. Broad blackish lateral stripe, bordered above by definite yellow streak; the latter is bordered above by a thin, definite dark streak. D, A and C yellowish; the C often very yellow, black bordered. Has appeared in aquarium trade as *R. dusonensis*. **Pd** 14-15, **Lls** 33-35, **Llp** 33-35, **Cp** 14. ++

R. trifasciata Popta, 1903. **Bo**. 2-3".Three-banded Rasbora, referring to dark bands on each side and along anal base and lower edge of caudal peduncle. Narrow black stripe from opercle to caudal base, gold line above it. Fins plain. *R. meinkeni* may be the same species; they seem nearly identical. *R. tobana* is also likely the same species. (See *R. meinkeni*). **Pd** 12, **Lls** 28-29, **Llp** 26-28, **Cp 12**. +

R. trilineata Steindachner, 1870. Scissorstail Rasbora. **M, Su, Th**. 4 $^1/_2$". Weak, thin dark stripe on posterior half of body, sometimes blending into a weak spot at base of tail fin, which has a black subterminal cross band on each lobe. This species is smaller, lighter-colored, and a bit deeper-bodied than *caudimaculata*, and has a well developed stripe over anal base. It is much larger and less pale-bodied than *spilocerca*. **Pd** 12-13, **Llp** 29-32, **Lls** 29-32. ++

Rasbora trilineata is the common Scissortail Rasbora which has been in the trade for almost 100 years. It is easily bred in the pools in Florida where it is merely thrown into the ponds with lots of vegetation. They do not bother their young if well fed.

Photo by Hans Joachim Richter.

Rasbora trilineata.

Photo by Dr. Herbert R. Axelrod.

Rasbora trilineata.

Photo by Klaus Paysan.

Photo by Dr. Harry Grier courtesy of FTFFA.

R. tubbi Brittan, 1954. Multi-blotched Rasbora. **Bo** (Brunei). 4". Stripe from snout essentially as in *cephalotaenia*, but dropping out in places along side; a secondary stripe along lateral line as far as anal base. Central **C** rays dark, **A** black tipped. **Pd** 13-14, **Llp** 34-35, **Lls** 34-35, **Cp** 14. ++

R. urophthalmoides Kottelat, 1991. Ocellated Dwarf Rasbora or Exclamation-point Rasbora. **IC, Su**(?). 1". Black stripe from opercle, broadest below dorsal and "pinching out" anteriorly and posteriorly, ending in a gold-ringed black spot at base of tail

This is the strain of *Rasbora trilineata* being bred in Florida.

A sketch of *Rasbora tubbi* which I originally described in 1954. It came from Brunei.

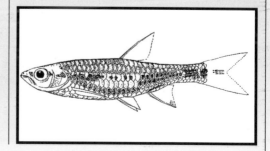

Rasbora tubbi.

Photo by Dr. Martin R. Brittan.

Rasbora urophthalmoides is an attractive small *Rasbora* which I call the Exclamation Point Rasbora. This is a female.

Photo by A. van den Nieuwenhuizen.

Photo by A. van den Nieuwenhuizen.

fin; this looks like an exclamation point "lying down". **D** and **A** with dusky anterior rays. **Pd** 11-12, **Llp** 0, **Lls** 27-28. This is the species reported in aquarium literature as *R. urophthalma*, the type-specimens of which are apparently of a dried-out "puntius." Rainboth (1996) shows *urophthalmoides* (fig.43) as having an orange-red background color; is this *brigittae*, which was originally described as a variety of *urophthalma?* +++

Rasbora urophthalmoides previously called *R. urophthalma*. This is a male.

Rasbora urophthalmoides.

Drawn by John Quinn.

Rasbora vaterifloris collected and photographed by Dr. Herbert R. Axelrod in Sri Lanka.

R. vaterifloris Deraniyagala, 1930. Sri Lanka Flower Rasbora. **SL**(s.e., in clear quiet forest streams). 2″. Dorsally green brown to purple. Ventrally pink to orange. **D, A,** and **C** orange or rosy. No stripes. Fins high and pointed. Body deep, sides compressed. **Pd** 12-13, **Llp** 3-4, **Lls** 25-26. Named after the yellow to reddish flower of the "Hal" tree (*Vateria*) of Sri Lanka. Pethiyagoda (1991) states: "There are also greenish, bluish, and two-colored morphs." The staturate red-purplish morph was once described *B. nigromarginata*, Meinken 1957. The subgenus *Rasboroides* was created by Brittan (1954) to contain this unique species. Kottelat (1993) has raised this subgenus to generic rank, hence the correct name for this species is *Rasboroides vaterifloris* (Deraniyagala). +++

Rasbora vaterifloris is a jewel-like, small rasbora. It is deep bodied and lacks the usual lateral stripe.

Photo by Edward Taylor.

Rasbora vaterifloris from the Nilwala River basin.

Photo by Dr. R. Pethiyogada.

R. vegae Rendahl, 1926. **Bo** (Sabah and Labuan I.). Kottelat considers this a junior synonym of *R. einthovenii*.

R. volzi Popta, 1905. **Bo** (w.). 3-4" Reticulate pattern well-developed. Larger specimens often lack a mid-lateral darkish streak, but sometimes may have a very weak one that is expanded on the posterior half of the body. The posterior narrow part of the streak expands into a blotch at the base of the caudal fin. The lateral streak is darker in small specimens. A black streak along anal base and a diagonal streak from upper opercle to pectoral origin (along "shoulder"). **Pd** 11-12, **Lls** 29-32, **Llp** 29-32, **Cp** 12. +

R. wijnbergi Meinken, 1963. Blacktip Rasbora. 1". Flanks silvery, darker above. Dorsal and anal yellowish-ochre with black tips. Caudal fin reddish basally. Described from an aquarium specimen "from Singapore." probably from **M** or **Bo,** which actually is a juvenile *caudimaculata* **Pd** 10, **Lls** 31, **Llp** 0, **Cp** 12. +

R. wilpita Kottelat & Pethiyagoda, 1991. Wilpita Rasbora. **SL.** 3 $^1/_2$". Mouth slanted strongly upward, center of lower jaw at level of top of orbit. Back brownish, sides Pearly bluish to pinkish. Broad blackish band from eye to caudal base. Intense black reticulate pattern directly over band, faint or absent esewhere. Fins pinkish-orange. **D, P**, and **A** with whitish tips. A rare species, known only from a short stretch of a threatened stream at Wilpita Estate in montane Sri Lanka. **Pd** 14, **Llp** 31-34, **Lls** 33-36, **Cp** 14. ++

BORARAS, PARLUCIOSOMA, AND RASBOROIDES

The tiny species of *Rasbora*, less than 20 mm. in standard length, that have, among other distinctive characters, a lower number of abdominal vertebrae than caudal ones (which is the reverse of the condition found in the other species of the genus), have been placed in a new genus, *Boraras* (an anagram of *Rasbora*) by Kottelat. These are *B. micros* (the type-species), *B. maculata, B. merah, B. brigittae,* and *B. urophthalmoides,* all seeming to be species of black, acid waters. The number of lateral line scales is reduced (22-28) and the lateral line is absent; these are characters commonly found in very tiny fishes, as an expression of parallel evolution. This appears to be a valid genus, but for the time being, largely as a matter of historical convenience, I prefer to keep the species in *Rasbora*.

Parluciosoma was created by Howes (1980) for some of the large species of *Rasbora* that have a bowl-shaped kinethmoid: included are *argyrotaenia* (his type species), *dusonensis, daniconius, cephalotaenia,* and *volzi*. Species considered by Howes as probably belonging to his new genus are *steineri, hubbsi. myersi,* and *tawarensis*. However, Howes did not at that time critically examine *R. rasbora,* the type-species of the genus *Rasbora,* nor did he examine in comparison other species beyond his limits of *Parluciosoma*. Kottelat has correctly pointed out that the "large silvery rasboras" are badly in need of revision. For this reason, *Parluciosoma* seems prematurely described, and it seems better to retain the species in *Rasbora* until the various phyletic lines can be properly sorted out.

Rasboroides (Brittan, 1954) was created to contain *Rasbora vaterifloris* which has the anal fin iii6 instead of iii5.

Horadandiya (Deraniyagala, 1943) has only one species, *H. atukorali*, found in Sri Lanka and extreme southern India. About 1" in length, it is brownish to greenish above, silvery below. Sides essentially plain, though in some lights a weak silvery metallic stripe, with a pale gold line above it, can be seen. Lateral line absent. Closely related to *Rasbora*, and some ichthyologists think *Rasboroides* should be united with it.

Rasbora wilpita is known only from a small section in a mountain stream in Sri Lanka.

Photo by Dr. R. Pethiyagoda.

FILIRASBORA, HORADANDIYA, MEGARASBORA, MICRORASBORA, RASBORICHTHYS, RASBORELLA, RASBORINUS, AND *SAWBWA.*

Filirasbora Fowler 1937, with two pairs of barbels on the upper jaw is a synonym of *Leptobarbus* Bleeker 1859.

Megarasbora (Günther, 1868) has only one species, *M. elanga*, from Bengal and Assam, which has usually been treated in *Rasbora*, often in *Megarasbora* as a subgenus. However, *Megarasbora* is a perfectly valid genus, characterized by tiny maxillary barbels and peculiar parallel striae on the scales. *M. elanga* is apparently more closely related to *Luciosoma* and other bariliines than to *Rasbora*.

Rasborichthys (Bleeker, 1857) contains two species. *R. helfrichii*, reaches 3-4", from Sumatra and Borneo. It has a sharp snout, fusiform body and long anal base;

***Luciosoma* species is one of the fishes often mistaken by aquarists as a *Rasbora*.**

Photo by Dr. Herbert R. Axelrod.

Microrasbora (Annandale, 1918) contains two tiny red fishes known only from Lake Inle in Burma, *rubescens* (the type-species) and *erythromicron*. They have no lateral line or only a very rudimentary one. The anal fin has 13-16 (8-13 branched) rays. Also included are *M. gatesi* Herre, 1939, and probably one or two undescribed species (also Burmese).

Raborella Fowler and Bean 1932 is based on one species (*dubia*) from "Oahu," where there are no native cyprinids! **Lls** 45, **Llp** 14, mouth protractile. Likely an invalid genus.

anal of 15-17 rays, ± 60 scales in lateral line. *R. altior* is deeper bodied with several thin streaks running longitudinally.

The genus *Rasborinus* (Oshima, 1920) has 2-3 forms from southeastern China and Hainan I. The lateral line is complete, the anal fin has 15-19 rays. There is a ventral keel between the pelvic and anal fins.

Sawbwa resplendens Annandale, 1918, is a unique species from Burma's Inle Lake. It is strawberry red in breeding color, scaleless, has no lateral line, a protrusible upper jaw, and a serrated dorsal spine. A very

Sawbwa resplendens is a unique species from Burma.

Photo by Mike Yamamoto.

A pair of *Sawbwa resplendens*. The male is the lower fish.

Photo by Mike Yamamoto.

Photo by Dr. Herbert R. Axelrod.

small fish, it may be most closely related to *Puntius.*

Except for *Horadandiya* none of the above genera thought to be related to *Rasbora,* or with "rasbor(a)" as a combining term in its name, seem to be.

Rasborichthys altior from Borneo.

Horadandiya atukorali.

Photo by Dr. Herbert R. Axelrod.

AQUARIUM REQUIREMENTS OF THE RASBORAS

Rasboras are perfect community tank fishes. They are peaceful and hardy, doing best if the water is slightly acid, but most do well in neutral or even slightly alkaline water. Rasboras can be kept at temperatures from 72-84°F, but remember that at the upper ranges they age faster and diseases seem to progress more quickly; 74-78°F is an ideal keeping range, 76-84°F or even 85°F for spawning. The only precautions to be taken are not to place the especially diminutive species (like *maculata*) in a tank with big bumptious forms (like some labeos and barbs), which, though otherwise good community fishes, might jostle, chase, or even eat such tiny fishes. Conversely, a few of the larger rasboras are such restless, active swimmers that they might upset a few very small, shy, retiring fishes. However, 95% of all the rasboras are community fishes. There is not a confirmed fin-nipper in the entire genus. They do not eat or uproot plants. Adequate

This magnificent aquarium was designed and photographed by Takashi Amano and appeared in Book 2 of his series NATURE AQUARIUM WORLD. The fishes are *Rasbora maculata* and *Sawbwa resplendens.*

Another of Takashi Amano's magnificent aquariums featuring *Rasbora pauciperforata*. This is one of the many aquariums designed and photographed by Takashi Amano and which appear in his series NATURE AQUARIUM WORLD.

swimming room should be given, and they should have the company of others of their kind, or other active fishes, or they are apt to remain quiet. Under optimum circumstances they show their best colors.

Any food is acceptable, either live or dried. The rasboras are less susceptible to swim bladder trouble from too long a period on dry food than the tetras, and less susceptible to digestive difficulties when overfed with rich live food (such as tubifex and white worms) than some of the essentially vegetarian fishes.

Brine shrimp, dapnia, white worms, tubifex, and other live foods are excellent in conditioning fishes for spawning, but none should be used exclusively. They should be alternated with each other and with well balanced dried foods.

So far as diseases are concerned, the usual ones occur in rasboras, but no more so than in other hardy fishes. The one disease that appears to be exceptionally hard to check is velvet, but so it is in other genera. Consult standard aquarium references for disease controls.

THE GENERAL BREEDING PATTERN

All rasboras have breeding patterns that consist of some minor variation of the following general scheme:

1. The sexes ripen, ovaries filling up with eggs, testes filling with sperm. This happens internally and becomes obvious externally when the females become swollen with mature eggs, when the males show interest in the females, and when both (the male especially) color-up. For the aquarist, live food will help in conditioning the spawners.

2. The potential parents begin to engage in courtship, the male being the aggressor. There usually is chasing, display by the male, or both. Coloration, which has been increasing in intensity as the fishes become ripe, now reaches its peak.

3. The spawners select mates, either pairing-off or two or three males spawning with the same female.

4. Semi-adhesive eggs, among which the male expels sperm as they are released, are deposited on the surface of broad-leaved plants or among masses of fine-leaved plants. Some usually fall to the bottom.

5. Spawning continues over several hours, until the female is spawned out; it may continue the following day. Spawners will generally ignore eggs if adequate food is available at spawning time; if spawners do bother ova it is usually with far less voracity than with the barbs. Aquarists may either (1) remove breeding fish after the initial spawning period; (2) remove the plants bearing the eggs to another aquarium after the initial spawning period is over (using a glass, rubber-bulbed, turkey baster or similar device to pipette up those eggs that have fallen to the bottom); or (3) if the aquarist elects to let the fish attempt to complete spawning the following morning (they are often not really completely spawned-out when they terminate activities after the initial spawning period the first day), they should be well fed with live food or walled off from the eggs. The former course (1) is easiest and safest.

6. With spawning completed, breeders, in nature, may not spawn until the following breeding season approximately a year later. These periods are under the control of climatic patterns and local ecological conditions. Typically, it appears that rasboras breed in nature shortly after the rainy season. At this time water conditions are optimum. Hardness is lowered, acidity is just right, there is plenty of water over plant-beds, and spawning areas are not choked with silt. Earlier, during the rainy season, water-flows may be torrential and fluctuate greatly from day to day and hour to hour; furthermore, a normally clear stream may be

heavy with silt. Later on, towards the end of the dry season, choice stream areas may go dry, there is more competition for space and food, in limestone areas water hardness builds up, in lowland forest regions acidity reaches a maximum, and, in non-flowing water, stagnation may occur. Aquarists, however, may breed their fishes all year round by artificially controlling the environment to duplicate as nearly as possible nature's seasonal optimum conditions. The minimum possible period between spawnings will depend upon the species, but averages about 3-6 weeks in the smaller species.

7. In general, most rasboras prefer a shaded aquarium for breeding (duplicating shaded spawning areas in the wild), although sunlight at one end during the morning sometimes stimulates spawning. Soft water, generally not over 5 grains of hardness (or less than 85 parts per million, since 1 grain equals 17 p.p.m.) is necessary, although some species spawn in far harder water; 2-3 grains is optimum. Water should be acid, from pH 5.6 to 6.9 being about right, although most rasboras will tolerate water more acid (as low as pH 5.0 or even 4.8), or even moderately alkaline (7.1-7.8); they do less well in any kind of alkaline water in relation to acid water, that is, moderately hard water is well tolerated, but soft water is preferable for spawning. Addition of soft water in aquaria apparently replicates the bringing-in of soft water during the rainy season in nature, which dilutes the water that has been becoming increasingly harder through concentration during the dry season. The addition of fresh water from rains may also reduce either excess alkalinity (stagnant, turbid, green, algae-choked water in nature is usually hard and alkaline) or acidity (clear, brown, transparent water in nature is usually acid). Whatever its previous condition, Mother Nature, through bringing in new water, alters it into the ideal state for spawning. The aquarist, by adding different water of the proper sort (or by putting his breeders into it), "bumps" them into spawning.

8. Eggs hatch in 18 to 40 hours depending on temperature and species. Young look like tiny glass splinters clinging to plants and sides of aquaria. They absorb the yolk sac over a period of about 24-48 hours, and become free swimming. At this time they begin to feed. Tiny species can be fed infusoria for a brief period, then newly-hatched brine shrimp; larger species can be started on the latter. Tiny sifted daphnia are good, too, and the finest of dried foods can also be used. As the young grow, progressively larger live and dried foods can be given.

EXAMPLES OF *RASBORA* SPAWNING PATTERNS

Breeding habits of some of the most popular species of *Rasbora* are given below. Notice that though they differ *in detail* from one another, they *conform basically* to the generalized breeding pattern already given. If you will look over the sections on breeding rasboras in the various aquarium books and the articles in various aquarium magazines, you will observe that all species show the same basic spawning pattern.

BREEDING *RASBORA HETEROMORPHA*

For many years this species resisted all attempts to spawn it. Although it has been spawned many times recently (including commercially), it still represents an interesting aquarium challenge, for it demands certain rather definite conditions.

Breeders should be chosen from young and vigorous stock, and should be conditioned on live food. When the female has filled with spawn and the male chases and displays in front of her, the breeders should be transferred into the prepared breeding tank. Single pairs, two males to a female, or small groups of 6-24 (with the males preferably in a ratio of about 2:1), may be used; in the latter case a considerably larger aquarium should be set up.

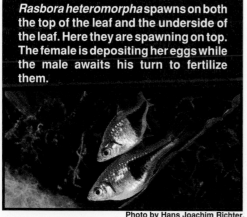

Rasbora heteromorpha spawns on both the top of the leaf and the underside of the leaf. Here they are spawning on top. The female is depositing her eggs while the male awaits his turn to fertilize them.

Photo by Hans Joachim Richter.

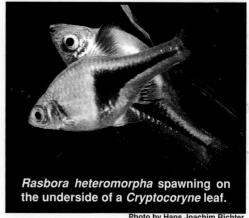

Rasbora heteromorpha spawning on the underside of a *Cryptocoryne* leaf.

Photo by Hans Joachim Richter.

The breeding aquarium should be of about 5-8 gallon size for pairs and trios, and of a 10-20 gallon size for spawning groups; deep, narrow tanks are not as good as wider, shallower ones. Cleanliness should be observed, but if eggs continue to be attacked by fungus, the following "sanitary regime" may be introduced. The aquarium should be thoroughly disinfected with a rock salt or alum bath, then completely rinsed out. If sand or marbles are used on the bottom they should be sterilized (boiling is easiest), then rinsed completely. Plants may be disinfected in a potassium dichromate dip, and either planted in sand or introduced in pots (which may be previously sterilized by boiling). Use of plants in pots allows for greater ease in setting-up of aquaria, introducing and removing plants, and keeping the bottom free of debris.

The spawning water should be brought to proper condition in a separate container. Either rainwater, distilled water, or aged tapwater may be used, providing the latter is not too hard; if so, it

Sometimes the spawning of *Rasbora heteromorpha* gets so vigorous that the eggs are thrashed loose from their position on the plant leaf.

Photo by Hans Joachim Richter.

may be diluted with distilled water or rainwater. The water is placed in an aquarium or large glass container that contains an inch or two of peat moss or sphagnum on the bottom, or is allowed to circulate repeatedly through a loose mass of peat in an outside filter until the desired pH is reached. Peat moss or sphagnum in the powdered, shredded, or whole state can be used but should be filtered through glass wool or filter paper (not charcoal) to remove debris. It often helps to boil the peat moss, especially the finer forms, before letting it steep, in order to speed up its saturation and keep it from floating; further, this process kills fungi and bacteria. *R. heteromorpha* has been spawned at pH readings of 4.8 to 7.5, but about 6.2 to 6.6 is a successful range. A hardness (DH) of 2-3 grains (about 30-50 p.p.m.) is about right, though it has been occasionally spawned in water up to 6-8 grains. Even distilled water run through peat moss will normally pick up a little bit of

hardness, but, if needed, it is easy to adjust the hardness by mixing rainwater or distilled water with tapwater. Use a hardness testing kit to check. The conditioned water may be boiled and cooled before adding it to the clean spawning tank. The plants are added and the tank set up so that it receives reduced light except for morning sunlight falling on one end.

Cryptocoryne species are the plants of choice in spawning *Rasbora heteromorpha*, but other broad-leaved plants can be substituted. These may either be planted in sand or in pots placed on clean sand, among marbles, or on a bare bottom. The last is satisfactory because of the ease of pipetting up infertile eggs and because *R. heteromorpha* rarely devours its own ova.

The breeders should be added in the late afternoon or early evening and the temperature gradually raised about 4 to 6 degrees Fahrenheit over the temperature of the community tank, or whatever aquarium the

Rasbora espei, laying eggs on the underside of a *Cryptocoryne* leaf. *Cryptocoryne* is the same plant as found with these fish in Thailand.

Photos by Karl Knaack.

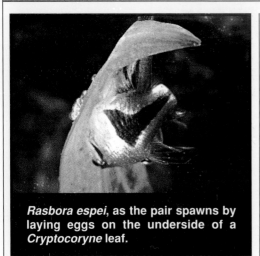

Rasbora espei, as the pair spawns by laying eggs on the underside of a *Cryptocoryne* leaf.

Photos by Karl Knaack.

spawners previously occupied; 76 to 80 degrees Fahrenheit is a good spawning temperature, although *heteromorpha* will spawn in water as high as 85 degrees Fahrenheit. Spawning will usually begin the following morning if the breeders have evidenced previous readiness to spawn. If they do not spawn within two or three days, drawing the water down half way and replacing it with fresh water or dropping the temperature gradually, then raising it again, will frequently "bump" them into spawning.

Spawning begins with the male displaying before the female and gently driving her, by nudging her side and by taking a position above her and rubbing his belly against her back, the top of her head, and her snout, forcing her downward. She then rubs the underside of a *Cryptocoryne* leaf with her belly, the male at first ignoring, then following her, taking a trembling side position, then arching about her body. As the eggs, a few at a time, are simultaneously expelled and

fertilized, they adhere to the leaf underside. Over a period of about two hours from 20 to 100 eggs are deposited in a number of different locations, a rare spawning reaching 200 to 300 eggs.

When spawning is finished it is best to remove the parents, although they may be given a good feeding of live good and held until the next day if the aquarist feels they may not have completed spawning; they may be walled off into an empty half of the aquarium if it is felt necessary, or the eggs, plants, pots, and all may be removed to another tank. The eggs hatch in about 18 to 24 hours at 80 to 82 degrees Fahrenheit. The newly hatched fry may be devoured by the parents before the latter begin to spawn for the second time the following morning. However, at 72 to 75 degrees Fahrenheit hatching is slowed to 30 to 36 hours. Generally, the best practice is simply to remove the parents after two to three hours of sustained spawning. They will be ready to breed again in three to six weeks.

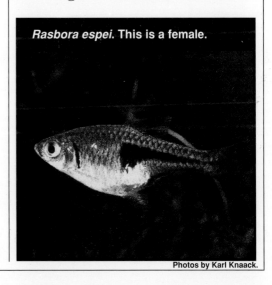

Rasbora espei. This is a female.

Photos by Karl Knaack.

Some eggs will fall to the floor of the aquarium. If these begin to fungus, they may be pipetted up and discarded. The others will hatch normally.

At first the young fry will look like tiny glass splinters. On the third or fourth day the young begin to feed. Infusoria, newly hatched brine shrimp, or pulverized hard boiled egg will do. The size of the food can gradually be increased to keep pace with the growth of the young.

Young reach breeding age in six to nine months. The species lives for a maximum of five to seven years under optimum conditions.

One breeder, using a group-spawning technique, uses large tanks, walling the breeders off in one half of the aquarium until the young are well along. He then removes the youngsters, leaving the adults to spawn again when ready, repeating the process up to a half-dozen times in the same water.

My own success has been best with the following combination: clean aquaria; completely ripe

Rasbora espei. This is a male.

Photo by Dr. Karl Knaack.

female and interested male, in one or two pairs; 10–gallon aquarium; *Cryptocoryne* in pots on bare floor; 76 to 80 degrees Fahrenheit; hardness 2-4 grains; parents conditioned on brine shrimp, white worms, and tubifex; parents removed at once on completion of first spawning session; and young fed infusoria and newly hatched brine shrimp.

The "sterility" fetish is ignored by many successful breeders, but cleanliness should be observed.

The female is the lower and more plump of the two *maculata*.

Photo by Hans Joachim Richter.

BREEDING *R. MACULATA*

The basic *Rasbora* spawning pattern, the same as for *heteromorpha*, should be followed. A smaller aquarium, as small as two gallons, may be used. Both broad-leaved (*Cryptocoryne, Sagittaria*, etc.) and narrow or fine leaved (*Nitella, Fontinalis, Eleocharis* or hair grass, masses or narrow-leaved *Vallisneria* or *Sagittaria*) aquarium plants have been used. When the breeding tank is satisfactorily set up (pH 6.5, DH 1-4 grains, 76 to 84 degrees Fahrenheit), the spawners are introduced in the evening. The following morning spawning begins, with the male displaying before the female, the pair quivering side-by-side, and the eggs being expelled one or two at a time onto the plants, often on the undersides of the leaves, occasionally in the open. Some cling to the plants, others fall to the bottom. Spawning is usually over in a half an hour, 15 to 30 ova being laid. If spawning continues later, another dozen eggs may be produced.

A tankful of *R. maculata* is an awsome sight.

Photo by Burkhard Kahl.

Eggs hatch in about 18 to 24 hours, the fry appearing as small, clinging glass splinters, and begin to feed on infusoria in another 24 to 48 hours, followed in a week or so by brine shrimp nauplii (newly-hatched young). Parents will spawn again in three weeks, but a rest of six weeks is better.

The spawning of *R. urophthalmoides* and other dwarf species is quite similar.

BREEDING *R. ARGYROTAENIA*

This is a prolific and easy-to-breed species, its pattern being typical for all of the medium and large-sized, elongated species. Use the basic spawning technique, with fine leaved plants preferred, although strands of broad-leaved ones can be used. The breeding aquarium should be of a minimum of five gallons (10 to 15 is better). While cleanliness should be maintained to avoid fungussing of eggs, the "ultra-cleanliness" desirable for *heteromorpha* is not usually necessary. Use pH 6.5, hardness of 2-4 grains. 76-80°F is a good temperature range.

The parents engage in an active chasing, the eggs being released during excited side-by-side trembling, with the eggs (often 100 to 300) being scattered widely among the plants. Most cling to the foliage, but many miss and fall to the bottom, or later fall from the leaves. They hatch in 24 to 30 hours at 78 degrees Fahrenheit, becoming free swimming and ready to feed in another 36 to 72 hours. Newly hatched brine shrimp are a fine first food. Infusoria, the finest sifted daphnia, or egg yolk will substitute.

R. daniconius, R. trilineata, and most other rasboras have a similar enthusiastic mating and scatter their eggs widely among plants. One spawn of a large pair of *daniconius* amounted to 478 ova, of which 423 hatched, and 304 reached $3/4$" in length, after which time the family was broken up by giving most of them away.

A pair of *Rasbora maculata* in pre-spawning play. The lower fish is the obvious female.

Photo by Hans Joachim Richter.

A TANKFUL OF RASBORAS

Several times I have had "community tanks" containing nothing but several species of rasboras. I had a 35-gallon tank with a dozen each of *R. hetermorpha, R. gracilis,* and *R. pauciperforata,* a half-dozen each of scissortails, *R. trilineata,* and quiet ember-red *R. kalochroma.* A half-dozen violet-hued, raggedy-lined *R. einthoveni* and spectacular bluish-bodied, orange-finned *R. vaterifloris* filled out the complement. Sometimes I substituted a dozen or half-dozen *R. dorsiocellata.* Four coolie loaches for bottom color and six zebra danios, or wild-type (bluish) pearl danios, for surface swimmers completed the suite.

The tank was so stunning that my dentist had one exactly like it set up in his office.

Substitutions can be made. The neon rasbora, *R. axelrodi,* would be a stunner, but is extremely hard to find in aquarium shops, so I have often substituted neon tetras and/or cardinal tetras for any of the above mentioned smaller rasboras, and I have at times used cherry barbs. A whole host of small peaceful cyprinids, tetras, and rainbowfishes will do. The nice thing is that none of these species are aggressive or predatory on their tankmates. So mix, match, and enjoy some of the loveliest of freshwater fishes.

A tankful of *Rasbora heteromorpha.*

Photo by Aqua Press, MP&C Piednoir

ACKNOWLEDGMENTS

See Brittan 1954 (reprinted 1971) for a historical review of work relating to *Rasbora* previous to 1952. Work since that date, principally by Eric Alfred, Gordon Howes, Mohd. Zakaria Ismail, K. C. Jayaram, Maurice Kottelat, Herman Meinken, A. G. K. Menon, Walter Rainboth, Darrell Siebert, and Tyson Roberts, has added greatly to our contemporary knowledge of the genus.

I especially wish to thank Marinus Boeseman, Maurice Kottelat, Han Nijssen, Walter Rainboth, Tyson Roberts, and Darrell Siebert for helpful conversations and/or correspondence. L.F. DeBeaufort, Albert W. Herre, Carl L. Hubbs, Herman Meinken, George S. Myers, and M.W.F. Tweedie, all now deceased except Tweedie, were of great help in years past. Herbert R. Axelrod and Warren E. Burgess of TFH Publications, and the ichthyology staffs of the California Academy of Sciences (San Francisco), the National Museum of Natural History (Washington, D. C.), the Museum of Natural History (London), the Rijksmuseum van Natuurlijke Historie (Leiden), the Zoologische Museum (University of Amsterdam), and the Zoologisches Museum von der Humboldt Universitat (Berlin), have aided greatly with access to specimens, collection records, and photographs.

DEDICATION

This book is dedicated to: the memory of Dr. George Sprague Myers, mentor, who taught me about rasboras; Dr. Herbert R. Axelrod, friend, who conceived of this book and prodded me to its completion; my wife, Ruth, who constantly helped and encouraged me when I needed it most; and to the millions of hobbyists who have kept or are now keeping the rasboras because they are so beautiful, peaceful and interesting.